CW00840904

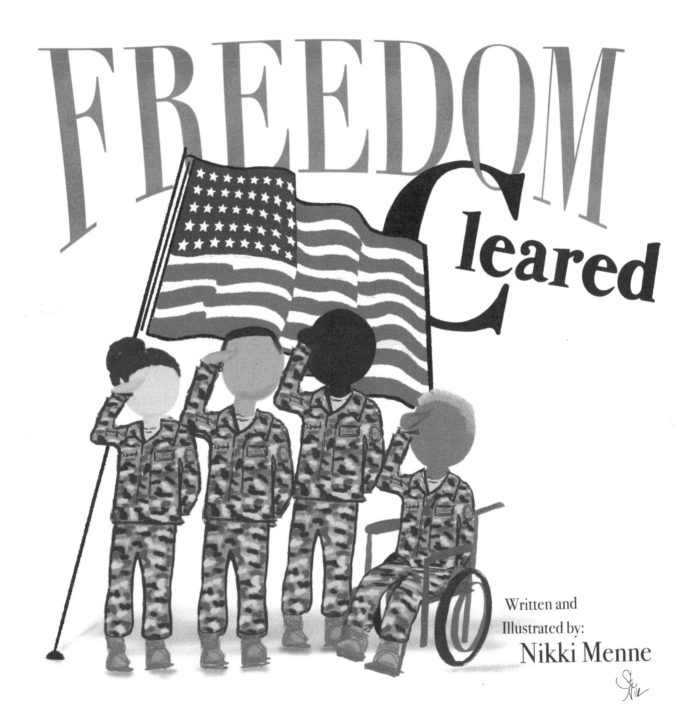

FREEDOM

Cleared

Written and
Illustrated by:
Nikki Menne

Freedom Cleared

ISBN: 978-1-7368473-7-4 (paperback)
ISBN: 978-1-7368473-0-5 (hardcover)

Library of Congress Number: 2022907086

Published by Reindeer Cleared Christmas Creations 2022
Text, Cover Design, and Illustrations © 2022 Nicole Menne
First edition 2022

Reindeer Cleared Christmas Creations
PO Box 262
Hasbrouck Heights, NJ
ReindeerCleared@gmail.com

To support of our military families and veterans visit:
www.ReindeerCleared.com

This book is dedicated to all the brave men and women
who have served, and continue to serve our country.

We are the land of the free because of your heroic service
and the sacrifices you've made.

Please let this book be a heartfelt thank you to you, and
a reminder of how much you are truly appreciated.
May God bless you and keep you safe always.
Thank you for being true heroes!

My grandfather, William H.
who fought in WWII.

Thank you, Grandpa. Love and miss you so much.

To purchase your Freedom Cleared bracelet visit:

ReindeerCleared.com

Each bracelet will help support our
military families and veterans.

I'd like to take a moment to thank you from the bottom of my heart,

I'm not even sure I know where to start.

You valued my freedom as much as your own,

You left behind family, friends, and your home.

All to make sure I could live my life free,

And have a chance to grow up to be all I can be.

Because of you, I am safe and protected each night.
Because of you, I feel safe to turn out my light.

Because of you, I can sit with my family
and share in a meal,

While your family feeling your absence
is all but too real.

A uniform only a few have put on,

An unwavering impact long after you're gone.

Each stripe and medal strategically placed,

Displaying your service and the danger you've faced.

I can sit in a classroom and learn from a book,

But it will never portray all that it took.

To put a stranger before yourself
without even a thought,

Is a true hero's calling and cannot be taught.

Only a person brave deep down in their soul,

Would put their life on the line and take on such a role.

You stare FEAR in the face and do not retreat,

And that is why we salute you and rise to our feet.

We celebrate you but not nearly enough,

You're built differently,
You're brave and you're tough.

If it's okay with you, I'd like to hold out my hand,
And give us both bracelets to remember your stand.

A reminder your service is why I am free,
A reminder to you, a forever thank you from me.

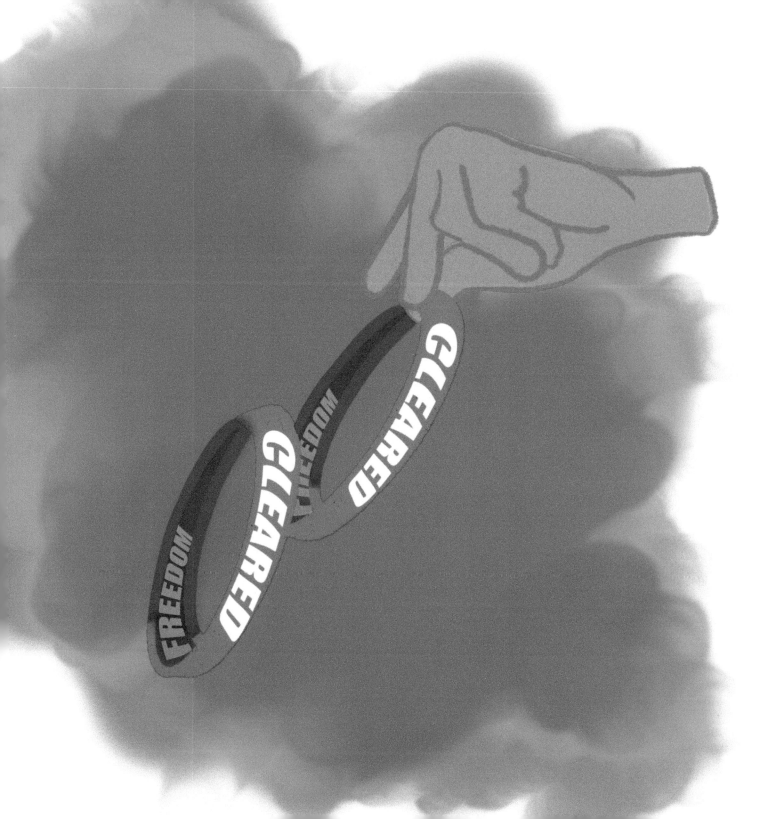

FREEDOM CLEARED
because of the sacrifices you've made,

FREEDOM CLEARED
because you were not afraid.

FREEDOM CLEARED
because you fought for me to be free,

FREEDOM CLEARED
because of your bravery.

SACRIFICE

FREE

STRONG

BRAVE

I know this bracelet is the least I can do,

But it's just a small way for me to thank you.

So when you look down at this bracelet
that we both wear,

Let it remind you of me and how much I care.

I will stop to thank each soldier and veteran I see,

Because you will always be true heroes to me.

Whether you fought land, sea, or air,

I promise to pause and show you I care.

You defend our country,
You bleed RED, WHITE, and BLUE.

You stand up to our enemies,
That's what you do.

True patriots come in all form, shape, and size,

But none hesitate to stand up and rise.

So whenever our anthem
is played throughout the land,

I will raise my hand to my chest
and with pride I will stand.

Because our freedom is not actually free,

It was built by each brave generation
that stood before me.

And tonight when I lay my head down to rest,

I'll pray for your safe return
and for you to be blessed.

Because not all heroes wear capes when they depart,
Some wear combat boots and the bravest of hearts.

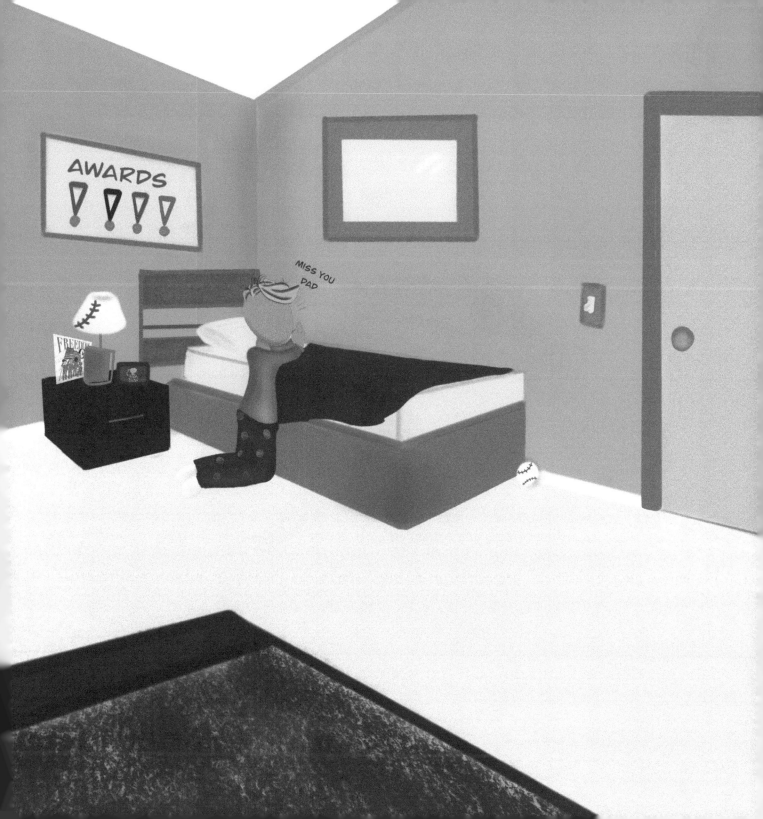

DRAW YOUR HERO!

DESCRIBE YOUR HERO!

1. _____

2. _____

3. _____

4. _____

5. _____

Lightning Source UK Ltd.
Milton Keynes UK
UKHW051711170522
403080UK00002BA/50